The

GOLDEN GATE Bridge

BUILDING A SAN FRANCISCO LANDMARK

HISTORICAL PHOTOGRAPHS BY TED HUGGINS

Pomegranate

SAN FRANCISCO

Pomegranate Communications, Inc.
Box 808022, Petaluma CA 94975
800 227 1428; www.pomegranate.com

Pomegranate Europe Ltd.
Unit 1, Heathcote Business Centre, Hurlbutt Road
Warwick, Warwickshire CV34 6TD, UK
[+44] 0 1926 430111; sales@pomeurope.co.uk

ISBN 978-0-7649-3787-3
Pomegranate Catalog No. AA352

Pomegranate publishes books of postcards on a wide range of subjects.
Please contact the publisher for more information.

Cover designed by Patrice Morris
Printed in China
15 14 13 12 11 10 09 08 07 06   10 9 8 7 6 5 4 3 2 1

To facilitate detachment of the postcards from this book, fold each card along its perforation line before tearing.

T he concept of bridging the mile-wide Golden Gate Strait between San Francisco and Marin County, California, was proposed as early as 1872 by railroad magnate Charles Crocker. In 1916 the idea was revived by San Francisco newspaperman James Wilkins, whose editorial campaign for a bridge caught the attention of San Francisco City Engineer M. M. O'Shaughnessy. O'Shaughnessy began a national inquiry among engineers regarding the feasibility of such a project. Most said the bridge couldn't be built; some said it was possible but would cost more than $100 million. One, Joseph B. Strauss, a designer of nearly four hundred spans, said such a bridge was not only feasible but could be built for $25 to $30 million.

On June 28, 1921, Strauss submitted preliminary sketches to O'Shaughnessy, estimating construction costs of $27 million. Strauss then dedicated himself to convincing civic leaders to go ahead with the plan. In November 1932, contracts totaling $23,843,905 were awarded, and on January 5, 1933, construction of the Golden Gate Bridge began.

As the bridge took shape over more than four years of work, the construction progress was captured on film by Ted Huggins, a public relations representative for Standard Oil Company and an enthusiastic proponent of the bridge. Thirty of his photographs—taken between 1934 and 1937—are reproduced in this book of postcards.

The Golden Gate Bridge opened on May 27, 1937. Today it stands as one of the most famous and beautiful engineering achievements in history.

The California Historical Society is a statewide membership-based organization. Its mission is to engage the public's interest and participation in collecting, preserving, and presenting art, artifacts, and written materials relevant to the history of California, and to support historical research, publication, and educational activities. With an extensive collection of books, maps, manuscripts, and printed ephemera, the Society's library serves more than 4,500 people each year. The CHS Photography Collection contains more than 500,000 images, including works by Eadweard Muybridge and Ansel Adams. Please visit www.calhist.org to learn more about the Society's collections, services, exhibitions, and publications.

The GOLDEN GATE Bridge

BUILDING A SAN FRANCISCO LANDMARK

North tower construction, 1934
Photograph by Ted Huggins

CA 94975

PETALUMA

BOX 808022

Pomegranate

The GOLDEN GATE Bridge

BUILDING A SAN FRANCISCO LANDMARK

Looking across the Golden Gate, April 1934
Photograph by Ted Huggins

BOX 808022   PETALUMA   CA 94975

Pomegranate

The GOLDEN GATE Bridge

BUILDING A SAN FRANCISCO LANDMARK

View of bridge construction and Fort Point
from Baker Beach, May 1934
Photograph by Ted Huggins

BOX 808022 PETALUMA CA 94975

Pomegranate

The GOLDEN GATE Bridge

BUILDING A SAN FRANCISCO LANDMARK

View of north tower, May 1934
Photograph by Ted Huggins

BOX 808022   PETALUMA   CA 94975

Pomegranate

The GOLDEN GATE Bridge

BUILDING A SAN FRANCISCO LANDMARK

Workers on south tower with view of north tower, 1935
Photograph by Ted Huggins

BOX 808022   PETALUMA   CA 94975

Pomegranate

The GOLDEN GATE Bridge

BUILDING A SAN FRANCISCO LANDMARK

Constructing catwalks, 1935
Photograph by Ted Huggins

BOX 808022 PETALUMA CA 94975

Pomegranate

The GOLDEN GATE Bridge

BUILDING A SAN FRANCISCO LANDMARK

Approach foundation and access trestle to south pier, 1935
Photograph by Ted Huggins

CA 94975

PETALUMA

BOX 808022

Pomegranate

The GOLDEN GATE Bridge

BUILDING A SAN FRANCISCO LANDMARK

Man waving atop completed north tower, 1935
Photograph by Ted Huggins

BOX 808022   PETALUMA   CA 94975

Pomegranate

The GOLDEN GATE Bridge

BUILDING A SAN FRANCISCO LANDMARK

Horizontal view of catwalks from Marin, November 1935
Photograph by Ted Huggins

BOX 808022 PETALUMA CA 94975

Pomegranate

The GOLDEN GATE Bridge

BUILDING A SAN FRANCISCO LANDMARK

View toward south tower, December 1935
Photograph by Ted Huggins

BOX 808022   PETALUMA   CA 94975

Pomegranate

The GOLDEN GATE Bridge
BUILDING A SAN FRANCISCO LANDMARK

Two workers standing on suspension cable, January 1936
Photograph by Ted Huggins

CA 94975

PETALUMA

BOX 808022

Pomegranate

The GOLDEN GATE Bridge

BUILDING A SAN FRANCISCO LANDMARK

View from Land's End, February 1936
Photograph by Ted Huggins

BOX 808022   PETALUMA   CA 94975

Pomegranate

The **GOLDEN GATE Bridge**

BUILDING A SAN FRANCISCO LANDMARK

View from south tower toward Baker Beach, March 1936
Photograph by Ted Huggins

BOX 808022   PETALUMA   CA 94975

Pomegranate

The GOLDEN GATE Bridge

BUILDING A SAN FRANCISCO LANDMARK

View of bridge construction with fog
Photograph by Ted Huggins

BOX 808022 PETALUMA CA 94975

Pomegranate

The GOLDEN GATE Bridge

BUILDING A SAN FRANCISCO LANDMARK

Workers on catwalks during cable spinning, March 1936
Photograph by Ted Huggins

CA 94975

PETALUMA

BOX 808022

Pomegranate

The GOLDEN GATE Bridge

BUILDING A SAN FRANCISCO LANDMARK

Spinning cable with view of San Francisco, June 1936
Photograph by Ted Huggins

BOX 808022   PETALUMA   CA 94975

Pomegranate

The GOLDEN GATE Bridge

BUILDING A SAN FRANCISCO LANDMARK

Workers spinning cable, 1936
Photograph by Ted Huggins

BOX 808022   PETALUMA   CA 94975

Pomegranate

The GOLDEN GATE Bridge

BUILDING A SAN FRANCISCO LANDMARK

Workers on cable catwalk, 1936
Photograph by Ted Huggins

CA 94975

PETALUMA

BOX 808022

Pomegranate

The GOLDEN GATE Bridge

BUILDING A SAN FRANCISCO LANDMARK

View of cargo ship passing beneath bridge construction,
June 1936
Photograph by Ted Huggins

BOX 808022 PETALUMA CA 94975

Pomegranate

The GOLDEN GATE Bridge

BUILDING A SAN FRANCISCO LANDMARK

View from Fort Point, 1936
Photograph by Ted Huggins

BOX 808022   PETALUMA   CA 94975

Pomegranate

^{The} # GOLDEN GATE Bridge

BUILDING A SAN FRANCISCO LANDMARK

View from east of Fort Point during raising of roadway,
October 1936
Photograph by Ted Huggins

BOX 808022   PETALUMA   CA 94975

Pomegranate

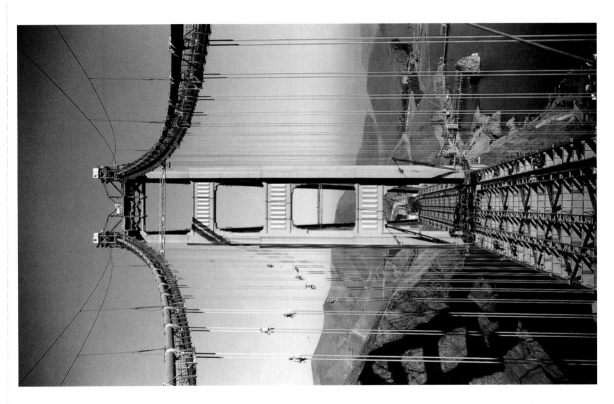

The **GOLDEN GATE** Bridge

Building a San Francisco Landmark

Workers painting suspender ropes above the completed
roadway, November 1936
Photograph by Ted Huggins

BOX 808022   PETALUMA   CA 94975

Pomegranate

The GOLDEN GATE Bridge

BUILDING A SAN FRANCISCO LANDMARK

View beneath bridge roadway with safety netting,
November 1936
Photograph by Ted Huggins

BOX 808022   PETALUMA   CA 94975

Pomegranate

The GOLDEN GATE Bridge

BUILDING A SAN FRANCISCO LANDMARK

View from east of Fort Point during paving of roadway,
January 1937
Photograph by Ted Huggins

Pomegranate

BOX 808022   PETALUMA   CA 94975

The GOLDEN GATE Bridge

BUILDING A SAN FRANCISCO LANDMARK

View of bridge from Baker Beach, January 1937
Photograph by Ted Huggins

Pomegranate

BOX 808022 PETALUMA CA 94975

The **GOLDEN GATE Bridge**

BUILDING A SAN FRANCISCO LANDMARK

Completed bridge, May 1937
Photograph by Ted Huggins

BOX 808022   PETALUMA   CA 94975

Pomegranate

The GOLDEN GATE Bridge
BUILDING A SAN FRANCISCO LANDMARK

Bridge elevator with workers and guests,
opening celebration, May 1937
Photograph by Ted Huggins

BOX 808022   PETALUMA   CA 94975

Pomegranate

The GOLDEN GATE Bridge

BUILDING A SAN FRANCISCO LANDMARK

Opening celebration, May 1937
Photograph by Ted Huggins

BOX 808022   PETALUMA   CA 94975

Pomegranate

The GOLDEN GATE Bridge

BUILDING A SAN FRANCISCO LANDMARK

Completed bridge with auto and
pedestrian traffic, 1937
Photograph by Ted Huggins

Pomegranate

BOX 808022   PETALUMA   CA 94975